Crosswords
For Kids

ARCTURUS

This edition published in 2019 by Arcturus Publishing Limited
26/27 Bickels Yard, 151–153 Bermondsey Street,
London SE1 3HA

ISBN: 978-1-78888-480-8
CH006440NT
Supplier 40, Date 0119, Print run 7798

Illustrated by Memo Angeles (Shutterstock)
Edited by Becca Clunes

Printed in the UK

CONTENTS

HOW TO SOLVE A PUZZLE

Welcome to the book of Super Crosswords! More than 160 puzzles are ready for you to solve, if you're up to the challenge.

To complete a crossword, solve the answer to each clue, and write your answers in the blank grid spaces (one letter per square). Start writing each answer in the square with the same number as the matching clue. Each clue has a number at the end of it—this tells you how many letters are in the answer. If the clue is in the 'Across' list, write your answer left-to-right. If the clue is in the 'Down' list, write your answer top-to-bottom.

You may see a semicolon (;) in some clues. The semicolon splits the clue into two parts, meaning you have not just one, but two clues to help you out!

If a clue refers to "an anagram," you'll have to do some unscrambling. An anagram takes all the letters of a word, puts them in a different order, and makes another word! For example, an anagram of "ocean" is "canoe."

Have fun!

1

ACROSS

1 Azure, navy, turquoise (4)

4 Tied ropes (5)

5 ___ and shoulders (4)

DOWN

2 Meal eaten in the middle of the day (5)

3 Additional person in a crowd scene (5)

Beginners

2

1	■	2	■	3
4				
	■		■	
5				
	■		■	

ACROSS
4 Patchwork bedcover (5)
5 Very upset (5)

DOWN
1 Evenly matched (5)
2 Metal bands worn on the fingers (5)
3 Hangs around; lodges (5)

Beginners

3

	1		2
3			
4			
5			

ACROSS

1 Bloom-to-be (3)

4 Unspecified item (5)

5 Very soft, wet dirt (3)

DOWN

1 Make a house (5)

2 Barking pets (4)

3 Part of a plant between the roots and leaves (4)

4

ACROSS

1 Plane's captain (5)

4 "___ it go!" (3)

5 No longer lost (5)

DOWN

2 Snow hut; Inuit dwelling (5)

3 Many times (5)

5

ACROSS

1 Remove in small bits;
   tool to break ice (4)

3 Dwelling made of logs (5)

4 Any plant growing in
   the wrong place (4)

DOWN

1 Crockery item from which
   food is eaten or served (5)

2 Boy or girl (5)

Beginners

6

ACROSS

1 Mix with a spoon (4)

4 Moist, succulent (fruit);
   interestingly scandalous (5)

5 Produce; add up to (4)

DOWN

2 Use or exercise the brain (5)

3 Fish with horizontally
   flattened bodies; sunbeam (3)

4 Press tightly together (3)

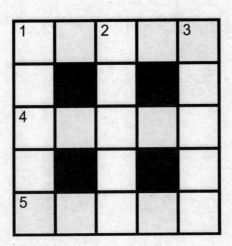

ACROSS

1 Showing courage; without fear (5)

4 Fruit, an important source of oil (5)

5 Having a menthol piquancy (5)

DOWN

1 Produce flowers (5)

2 Creature from another world (5)

3 Opponent; the opposite of "friend" (5)

8

ACROSS

3 Stood completely still; became icy (5)

4 Hours between evening and morning (5)

DOWN

1 Clear one's throat or chest; cold symptom (5)

2 Sharply curved (4)

3 Successfully search for (4)

Beginners

1	**2**		**3**	
4				
5				

ACROSS

1 Edible, tentacled marine creature; calamari (5)
4 Sporting contests (5)
5 Ability learned by training (5)

DOWN

2 Duck sound (5)
3 Perfectly suited (5)

Beginners

10

ACROSS

3 Decorative award (5)

5 Sticky substance; something you chew (3)

6 Leaves of a book (5)

DOWN

1 Started (5)

2 Spitting desert animal (5)

4 Used a spade (3)

Beginners

11

ACROSS
3 Not heavy or dark (5)
5 Superhero magazine (5)

DOWN
1 The opposite of "white" (5)
2 Small, thin branch of a tree (5)
4 Diamond or emerald (3)

Beginners

12

ACROSS

3 Open and shut both eyes quickly (5)

5 Light boat with sails (5)

DOWN

1 Do as one is told (4)

2 Female wizard (5)

4 Flying toy; bird of prey (4)

Beginners

13

ACROSS

1 With the power (to do something) (4)

4 Person who decides the result of a competition (5)

5 Headgear; boater and fez, for example (4)

DOWN

2 Bushy tail of a fox (5)

3 Number of legs on a spider (5)

14

ACROSS

4 Having good fortune (5)
5 Large fruit with pulpy flesh (5)

DOWN

1 Feather worn as an ornament;
long cloud of smoke (5)

2 Climb; weighing device (5)

3 Wild mammal of Africa,
similar to a dog (5)

15

ACROSS

1 Firm flesh around the roots of the teeth (3)

4 Young human (5)

5 Not "in" (3)

DOWN

1 Feeling of having done wrong (5)

2 Put together; an anagram of "Edam" (4)

3 Rebound, like sound (4)

Beginners

16

ACROSS

1 Hill feature; an anagram of "lopes" (5)

4 Small bed (3)

5 Psalms; songs sung in Christian churches (5)

DOWN

2 Like lottery winners (5)

3 Affect (an accent); don (clothes) (3,2)

Beginners

17

ACROSS

1 Word that can go before "salts" or "towels" (4)

3 Slow creature, often found in gardens and rockpools (5)

4 Yellow part of an egg (4)

DOWN

1 Long-necked stringed instrument (5)

2 Dense (of fog) (5)

Beginners

18

ACROSS

1 Contented cat sound (4)

4 Tackle a mountain (5)

5 Small insects (4)

DOWN

2 Putting into action; utilizing (5)

3 Barbecue seasoning; wipe or move over something with pressure (3)

4 Young bear (3)

Beginners

1		2		3
	███		███	
4				
	███		███	
5				

ACROSS

1 Ability (to do something);
  ___ nap (5)

4 Shade of purple;
  fragrant plant (5)

5 Giddy; confused (5)

DOWN

1 Heaped up (5)

2 Type of ballroom dance (5)

3 Stony; craggy (5)

Beginners

20

ACROSS

3 Scrape gently; feed on grass (5)

4 ___ outside the box (5)

DOWN

1 Bowl-shaped container (5)

2 Nip (like a bird); little kiss (4)

3 Entrance to a field (4)

Beginners

21

ACROSS

1 Adult or child; ___ being (5)

4 Feeling as if one wants to scratch (5)

5 Move smoothly and easily (5)

DOWN

2 Up to a time (5)

3 Suffered from sore muscles (5)

Beginners

22

ACROSS

3 Yellow, oval-shaped sour fruit (5)

5 Metal element, symbol Sn; material used to make toy soldiers (3)

6 Containers used to move a house with (5)

DOWN

1 Board a bus or train (3,2)

2 Beehive product (5)

4 Combine into one (3)

Beginners

23

ACROSS

3 In the area (5)

5 Great weather for flying a kite (5)

DOWN

1 Circus funny person (5)

2 Has fun; stage shows (5)

4 Container for beans (3)

Beginners

24

ACROSS

3 Ceramic material; very large country (5)

5 Mental activity during sleep (5)

DOWN

1 Sour, corrosive solution (4)

2 Known fact (5)

4 Elbows' locations (4)

Beginners

25

ACROSS

1 Halt; put off forever (4)

4 Large, natural stream of water (5)

5 "Here ___ nothing!" (4)

DOWN

2 Object; item (5)

3 Serving of cake (5)

Beginners

26

ACROSS

4 Instrument, can be upright or grand (5)

5 Quacking waterbirds (5)

DOWN

1 Garden shovel (5)

2 Wrist-clock; observe (5)

3 Long-necked waterbird (5)

Beginners

27

ACROSS

1 Chin bone (3)

4 Sip or gulp (5)

5 Orangutan, or chimpanzee, for example (3)

DOWN

1 Fruit's liquid (5)

2 Become conscious after sleeping (4)

3 Thought; "just an ___" (4)

Beginners

28

ACROSS

1 Swatters' victims (5)

4 Male child (3)

5 Material to make clothes with (5)

DOWN

2 Place for washing instructions (5)

3 African country with the capital Cairo (5)

Beginners

ACROSS
1 Coil of hair (4)
3 Material worth; cherish (5)
4 Not naturally that shade (4)

DOWN
1 Insane; very enthusiastic (5)
2 Ball-shaped (5)

Beginners

30

ACROSS

1 Warm-blooded egg-layer (4)

4 Joined links of metal (5)

5 Banana skin (4)

DOWN

2 Mental picture; camera product (5)

3 Home for lions, bears, or wolves (3)

4 Drinking vessel (3)

Beginners

31

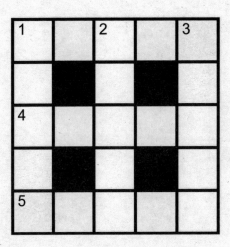

ACROSS

1 Rub hard; wash thoroughly (5)
4 Striped horse-like animal (5)
5 Moat without water (5)

DOWN

1 Having specified dimensions (5)
2 Android or cyborg; man-made machine (5)
3 Sandy area (5)

Beginners

32

ACROSS

3 Railway locomotive (5)

4 Covered with wet earth (5)

DOWN

1 Musical groups; stripes or hoops (5)

2 Child with no siblings (4)

3 Not wild; an anagram of "meat" (4)

Beginners

33

ACROSS

1 Steep rock face (5)

4 Like a good comedian (5)

5 Follow after, especially if running (5)

DOWN

2 Enjoy a joke; show amusement (5)

3 Discovers by chance (5)

Beginners

34

ACROSS

3 Chill out; ease tension (5)

5 Dunk underwater quickly (3)

6 Thoughts, concepts, or notions (5)

DOWN

1 Plaything consisting of a child's toy bear, usually stuffed (5)

2 Tokyo's country, sometimes called Nippon (5)

4 Tell an untruth (3)

ACROSS

3 Large, American thrush with a red breast; small European songbird with a red breast (5)

5 Little lake boat (5)

DOWN

1 Amount charged for an item (5)

2 Heavenly being (5)

4 Variety of sweet cake (3)

Beginners

36

<!-- Crossword grid -->

ACROSS

3 Grown-up person (5)

5 Celebration; gathering of people (5)

DOWN

1 Group of tents (4)

2 Move fast; rush (5)

4 Things for children to play with, such as small cars, balls, etc. (4)

Beginners

37

ACROSS

1 Totals up (4)

4 Coal worker (5)

5 Young female human being (4)

DOWN

2 Action; engaged in (5)

3 Control direction; direct a course (5)

Beginners

38

ACROSS

4 Conversation starter; phone greeting word (5)

5 Small amount, in a recipe; squeeze tightly between the fingers (5)

DOWN

1 Circle, square, or hexagon, for example (5)

2 Airborne vehicle; wood-smoothing tool (5)

3 Flying insects that are drawn to light (5)

Beginners

39

ACROSS

1 Male sheep (3)

4 Typical; an anagram of "luaus" (5)

5 Barbecue pit leftover (3)

DOWN

1 Wild and irregular; bumpy (5)

2 Mammal mothers produce this to feed their babies (4)

3 Very large brass wind instrument (4)

Beginners

40

ACROSS

1 Time-teller (5)

4 Trap spun by a spider (3)

5 Side that is forward (5)

DOWN

2 Less high (5)

3 Bedroom on a ship (5)

41

ACROSS

1 Say words to a tune and rhythm (4)

3 Of great size; an anagram of "glare" (5)

4 Thaw (4)

DOWN

1 Just-in-case extra item (5)

2 Time of day after evening (5)

Beginners

42

ACROSS

1 Large, long-necked waterbird; adult cygnet (4)

4 Possessed entirely; an anagram of "endow" (5)

5 Hurry; haste (4)

DOWN

2 Planes, birds, and insects have these to help them to fly (5)

3 Quick bob of the head (3)

4 Belonging to us (3)

43

¹		²		³
	■		■	
⁴				
	■		■	
⁵				

ACROSS

1 Group (of bananas) (5)

4 As far as something can go (5)

5 Side-to-side measurement (5)

DOWN

1 The opposite of "above" (5)

2 Called; an anagram of "amend" (5)

3 Cage for animals to live in (5)

Beginners

44

ACROSS

3 Fetch; carry here (5)

4 Smooth and reflective (5)

DOWN

1 Call on someone; be a guest (5)

2 Not pretty to look at; like Hans Christian Andersen's duckling (4)

3 Better than good (4)

45

ACROSS

1 Bike wheel feature; said (5)

4 Artist's substance; wall covering (5)

5 Not far away (5)

DOWN

2 Gemstone made by an oyster (5)

3 Sorts; types (5)

46

ACROSS

3 Large book of maps (5)

5 Took cover; tucked away (3)

6 Bushes forming a fence (5)

DOWN

1 Not this or that (5)

2 Emblem of belonging (5)

4 Eye protection; pot top (3)

Beginners

47

ACROSS

3 Unhappy or distressed; knock over (5)

5 Not decorated; no-frills (5)

DOWN

1 Young dog (5)

2 Small lump of rock (5)

4 Large body of salt water partially enclosed by land (3)

Beginners

48

1		2		
3				4
5				

ACROSS

3 Playground equipment (5)

5 Move in time to music (5)

DOWN

1 Second-hand; no longer new (4)

2 Very large mythical figure (5)

4 Became larger (4)

Beginners

49

1	■	**2**	■	**3**
4				
	■		■	
5				
	■		■	

ACROSS

4 Number in a trio or hat trick (5)

5 Melody or harmony (5)

DOWN

1 Postage label (5)

2 Emblem on the Swiss flag (5)

3 Instruct; an anagram of "cheat" (5)

50

ACROSS

1 The opposite of "good" (3)

4 Male monarchs (5)

5 Salary or wages; settle a bill (3)

DOWN

1 Friendly name for a rabbit (5)

2 Writing table, often found in classrooms (4)

3 Gait in which steps and hops alternate (4)

Beginners

ACROSS

1 Skilled and competent (4)

4 Indian-style dish (5)

5 Limited period of time, four years for a president (4)

DOWN

2 The opposite of "sharp" (5)

3 Mistake; reason to reboot (5)

Gentle

52

ACROSS

1 Feeling unhappy (3)
4 Come to pass; come to one's mind (5)
6 Tear violently (3)
7 Of a fire, extinguished (3)
8 Cut thinly (5)
9 Dark bread grain (3)

DOWN

1 Predatory sea fishes (6)
2 Clever sea mammal (7)
3 Tenth month of the year (7)
5 Toy; an anagram of "latter" (6)

Gentle

53

ACROSS

1 Female monarch; female cat (5)
4 Large, flightless bird from Australia (3)
5 Delicious tree-fruit (5)
6 Slogan or saying as guiding principle (5)
7 Female deer (3)
8 Big; an anagram of "regal" (5)

DOWN

1 Half of one half (7)
2 Blow up (7)
3 Sharp, pointed implement (usually steel) (6)
4 Hard, smooth coating over a tooth (6)

Gentle

54

ACROSS

3 Frozen spike; stalactite (6)
5 Delighted in or relished (7)
8 Most people have one of these on each hand (6)

DOWN

1 Two plus three (4)
2 Eight-limbed sea creature (7)
4 Sensory organ on a snail's stalk (3)
6 Fishing item; meshed fabric (3)
7 Wipe with a dry cloth (4)

55

ACROSS

4 Contrast two or more things together, and list any differences (7)

5 Form of water (3)

6 Make a small incision (3)

7 Denied access (7)

DOWN

1 Biggest kind of penguin (7)

2 Thin batter fried on both sides in a hot skillet or griddle (7)

3 Made warm; angry or impassioned (6)

4 Mounts, rises (6)

Gentle

56

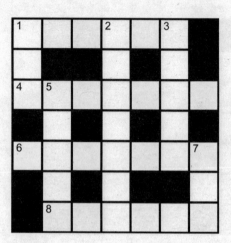

ACROSS

1 Pieces of poetry or lyrics with similar-sounding endings (6)
4 This often accompanies lightning in a storm (7)
6 With little or no sound (7)
8 Stands for paintings (6)

DOWN

1 Common rodent (3)
2 Long-tailed primates (7)
3 Witch's formula; short period of time (5)
5 Building used as a home (5)
7 Positive response to a question (3)

57

ACROSS

2 Hand covering; baseball player's tool (5)

4 Large, rounded mass of rock (7)

5 Fortunate (5)

DOWN

1 Gather; fetch (7)

2 Low, menacing noise from a dog or other animal (5)

3 Each one, without exception (5)

Gentle

58

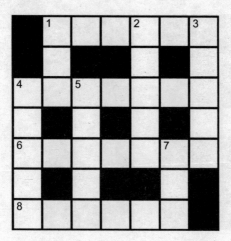

ACROSS

1 Elevated platforms; puts on a play (6)
4 Place where goods are made (7)
6 Role model; set a good ___ (7)
8 Separated into two equal parts (6)

DOWN

1 Adriatic, for example (3)
2 Number of people classed together (5)
3 Fashion (5)
4 Not canned or frozen (5)
5 Move on your hands and knees (5)
7 Was in first place (3)

Gentle

59

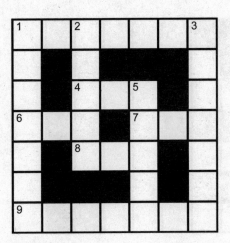

ACROSS

1 Direction-finding instrument (7)
4 Narrow opening (3)
6 Move over snow (3)
7 Have a debt to pay (3)
8 Unit of a train or roller coaster (3)
9 Brushed against (7)

DOWN

1 Nearest (7)
2 Wizards and witches practice this (5)
3 Reacted to dust or pollen (7)
5 Covered entrance to a building (5)

Gentle

60

ACROSS

1 Identical in quantity (5)
5 Person from Kenya or Morocco, for example (7)
6 Chocolate-chip or oatmeal-raisin (7)
7 Remains (in a place) (5)

DOWN

2 With rapid movements (7)
3 Very surprised (6)
4 Strenuous physical or mental exertion (6)

Gentle

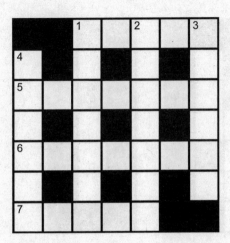

ACROSS

1 Has on, as clothing (5)
5 Division of book (7)
6 Go off, like a bomb (7)
7 Rises and falls of the sea;
  they can be high or low (5)

DOWN

1 Enclosed securely in a
  covering of paper (7)
2 Book writers (7)
3 Road lined with houses (6)
4 Style of pronunciation (6)

Gentle

62

ACROSS

3 "Weeping" tree that grows near water (6)
4 Trip; voyage (7)
6 Small creature, such as a beetle or fly (6)

DOWN

1 Frightened; terrified (7)
2 Distant in space or time (4)
3 Doctor ___; what person? (3)
4 Become part of; come together (4)
5 Munch, consume (3)

Gentle

63

ACROSS

1 Person receiving medical treatment; able to wait (7)
4 Covered with slimy or dirty gunk (5)
7 Unbaked bread (5)
9 Type of power or weapon (7)

DOWN

1 Symbol of Halloween (7)
2 Black or blue fluid, kept in a pen (3)
3 Class instructor (7)
5 Large, edible fish (3)
6 The opposite of "me" (3)
8 Harry Potter's pet (3)

Gentle

64

ACROSS

1 Carrier for liquids;
  ___ and spade (6)
4 Reviewer of text (6)
7 Taking to the skies (6)
8 Fine strand of yarn (6)

DOWN

1 Honeymakers (4)
2 Feverish cold; relax (5)
3 Black liquid; an
  anagram of "rat" (3)
5 Oil-producing fruit (5)
6 Grew older (4)
7 In good condition (3)

Gentle

65

ACROSS

1 Not flexible (5)
5 Section of a felled tree (3)
6 AM/FM device (5)
7 Pungent vegetable (5)
8 Body part that picks up sounds (3)
9 Power of vision (5)

DOWN

1 Petted; rubbed gently (7)
2 In a house; not outside (7)
3 Moving smoothly; an anagram of "wolfing" (7)
4 In contrast to; touching (7)

Gentle

66

ACROSS

1 Drink, usually of Chinese or Indian origin (3)
4 "Too many ___ spoil the broth" (5)
6 Another word for "farewell" (7)
7 Make an outline of (5)
8 Expected (3)

DOWN

1 Showed how; gave knowledge to (6)
2 Big-top tumbler (7)
3 Multiplied by two (7)
5 Arm of a shirt or jacket (6)

Gentle

67

ACROSS

1 Very alike, but not identical (7)
4 Protest; thing (6)
7 Land; earth (6)
8 Track or field sportsperson (7)

DOWN

1 Foot covering (4)
2 Military rank (5)
3 Hill-building insect (3)
5 Make happen (5)
6 Lazy; an anagram of "lied" (4)
7 Come into the possession of (3)

Gentle

68

ACROSS

1 Butterfly relatives (5)
5 Suspicious or frightened of being displaced by a rival (7)
6 Scent, usually pleasant and sometimes applied to the skin (7)
7 Warning (5)

DOWN

2 Removed wrapping (6)
3 Providing assistance, or serving a useful function (7)
4 Hottest season of the year (6)

Gentle

ACROSS

1 Munched (6)
4 Light wind (6)
7 Selected (6)
9 Generic name for fine paper-cloth used to catch sneezes (6)

DOWN

1 Taxi (3)
2 Which place? (5)
3 ___-sea diver (4)
5 Boulders (5)
6 Word after beauty or blind; small mark (4)
8 Stain a different shade (3)

70

ACROSS

4 Make up your mind (6)
6 One more (7)
7 Camembert or Cheddar, for example (6)

DOWN

1 Develops; turns into (7)
2 Most elevated; an anagram of "eighths" (7)
3 Small, soft fruit (5)
5 Backyard game for two (5)

Gentle

71

ACROSS

1 Stiff paper (4)
3 Bend forward at the waist (3)
5 Punctuation mark (,) (5)
6 Unwanted sound (5)
7 From the past (3)
8 Food with fragile shells (4)

DOWN

1 Bird; sort of clock (6)
2 Jog the memory (6)
3 Cooking in an oven (6)
4 There are two of these on a bicycle, and only one on a unicycle (6)

Gentle

72

ACROSS

1 Settled a debt; gave money (4)
4 Acorn tree (3)
6 Married man; wife's partner (7)
7 Golf ball support (3)
8 Bolt; rush (4)

DOWN

2 Quantity (6)
3 Increased by 100 percent (7)
5 Midwest US state (6)

Gentle

73

ACROSS

1 It might prevent a boat from drifting off (6)
5 Changed, varied (7)
6 Eight-legged arthropods (7)
7 Four times twenty (6)

DOWN

2 No amount at all (7)
3 Gather a ripened crop (7)
4 Goes on horseback; an anagram of "dries" (5)
5 Supermarket division (5)

Gentle

74

ACROSS

2 Computer language (5)
5 Dish baked in a pastry-lined pan (3)
6 Percussion instruments (5)
7 Lead; direct (5)
8 Place to see animals (3)
9 At that place (5)

DOWN

1 Vertical; type of piano (7)
2 Hour for sleep (7)
3 Press firmly (7)
4 Place to keep pins; soften (an impact) (7)

Gentle

75

ACROSS

1 Large ocean mammals (6)
4 Cheetah, compared to other animals (7)
6 Egyptian royal tomb (7)
8 Brightly feathered tropical bird with a short, hooked beak (6)

DOWN

1 Tired and jaded (5)
2 Paintings, sculptures, and the like (3)
3 Took a seat (3)
5 Rapid (5)
6 Burst suddenly (3)
7 Word that can precede "guitar" or "kiss" (3)

Gentle

76

ACROSS

4 Continent between Asia and the Atlantic Ocean (6)

5 Rebounded (7)

8 Succeed in avoiding (6)

DOWN

1 "Doing" word, in grammar (4)

2 Link together (7)

3 This place (4)

6 Kitchen appliance (4)

7 Sketched; ended a game with both teams on the same score (4)

Gentle

ACROSS

1 Brief rainfall; bathroom fixture (6)
4 Chic; stylish (7)
7 Very large (7)
9 Game; an anagram of "sent in" (6)

DOWN

1 Old-fashioned method of powering engines, especially trains (5)
2 Unwraps; unfolds (5)
3 Race; flee (3)
5 Not of this planet (5)
6 Tall, woody plants (5)
8 Part of a play (3)

Gentle

ACROSS

4 Personal belief or view (7)
5 Got into clothes (7)
8 Use your lungs (7)

DOWN

1 Part of a sentence (4)
2 Not common or ordinary (7)
3 Organ of smell (4)
6 In very short supply (4)
7 Hoofed grazing animal with branched bony antlers (4)

Gentle

ACROSS

4 Yellow powder on flowers; cause of hay fever (6)

6 Insignificant talk (7)

7 Instructions for cooking a dish (6)

DOWN

1 Astronaut's workplace (5)

2 Rested on top of the water (7)

3 Sure; specific (7)

5 "Go" signal; eco-friendly (5)

Gentle

80

ACROSS

3 Outdoor meal (6)
5 Milked animal (3)
6 A building where guests can pay for lodging (5)
8 Writing implement (3)
9 Frightened; an anagram of "cedars" (6)

DOWN

1 Genies traditionally grant three of these if you release them (6)
2 Small rodents (4)
4 Less hot (6)
7 At some earlier time (4)

Gentle

81

ACROSS

1 Container for liquids; any watercraft (6)
5 Apply in a thin layer with a knife, e.g. ___ butter on bread (6)
7 Freedom from illness; wellbeing (6)
8 Pit diggers (6)

DOWN

2 Clearly describe a process (7)
3 Cardigan or pullover, for example (7)
4 Polite name for a woman (4)
6 Those people (4)

Gentle

82

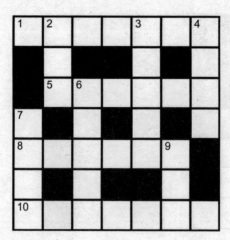

ACROSS

1 Dusty spiders' lairs (7)
5 Fire-breathing mythical creature (6)
8 Move from one place to another (6)
10 Brief communication, such as a text (7)

DOWN

2 Unusual (3)
3 Large bird of prey (5)
4 Grains of rock, often found on beaches (4)
6 Routes for vehicles (5)
7 Smallest part of a molecule (4)
9 Lower limb (3)

Gentle

83

ACROSS

2 Cup with a handle (3)
4 Bedtime tale (5)
5 Ocelot, lion, or tabby (3)
6 Pull something on a rope behind you (3)
7 Third month of the year (5)
8 ___ date (deadline) (3)

DOWN

1 Dress-up outfit (7)
2 Inexplicable happening (7)
3 Increase in size; development (6)
4 Between first and third (6)

Gentle

84

ACROSS

1 Dance movement (4)
5 Having much money (4)
6 Food preparation room (7)
7 Hospital places; areas of ground where flowers are grown (4)
8 Balanced equally (4)

DOWN

2 Taught a skill; worked at a sport (7)
3 Exact; accurate (7)
4 Subject such as biology or chemistry (7)

Gentle

85

ACROSS

2 This one plus that one (4)
5 Owns; possesses (3)
7 Runway walker (5)
8 The opposite of "buys" (5)
9 Shade of brown (3)
10 Border; team (4)

DOWN

1 Selects; picks (7)
3 Most aged; first-born of siblings (6)
4 Single portion of food (7)
6 Showed amusement or delight (6)

Gentle

86

ACROSS

3 Carousel figures (6)
6 Set of cards; fill a suitcase (4)
7 Bouncy toy (4)
9 One of the primary pigments; hue of lemons or sunflowers (6)

DOWN

1 First school day of the week (6)
2 Vegetable; an anagram of "ape" (3)
4 Accident with liquid (5)
5 Place to learn; group of fish (6)
8 Allow; permit (3)

Gentle

87

ACROSS

1 Plant grown on a large scale by farmers (4)

4 Remainder; relax (4)

6 Spectrum in the sky (7)

7 Provided without charge (4)

8 Step of a ladder (4)

DOWN

2 Restore to good working order; mend (6)

3 Computer output device; machine to make physical copies of electronic files (7)

5 Talked; voiced; said (6)

Gentle

88

ACROSS

1 Go round and round (4)
4 Not liquid or solid (3)
6 Double; more than once (5)
7 Breathing, and with a pulse (5)
8 "___ you later!" (3)
9 Eternally; for ___ (4)

DOWN

2 Awards (6)
3 Knitting tool (6)
4 Car shelter or repair place (6)
5 Thin line (6)

Gentle

ACROSS

1 Painting tool (5)
4 Item for rowing a boat (3)
6 Bend (5)
7 Huge sea (5)
8 "Neither here ___ there" (3)
9 Car engine (5)

DOWN

1 Disc for pushing or fastening (6)
2 Soldier's or schoolchild's outfit (7)
3 Most heated (7)
5 Competitor in a foot-race (6)

Gentle

90

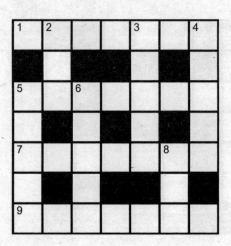

ACROSS

1 Stood against (7)
5 Like the pyramids (7)
7 Reptiles with bony shells and flipper-like limbs (7)
9 Place of higher education (7)

DOWN

2 Tuck; metal fastener (3)
3 One of the senses (5)
4 Fruits of the palm (5)
5 Space inside a house roof (5)
6 Reefs are made of this (5)
8 Platypus nest item (3)

Gentle

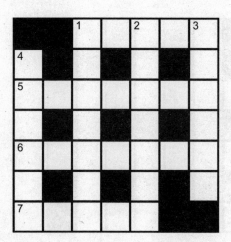

ACROSS

1 Mails; posts (5)
5 Offered hospitality; asked to dinner (7)
6 Extraordinary, remarkable event (7)
7 Toy children (5)

DOWN

1 More than a couple but not many (7)
2 Sees; an anagram of "section" (7)
3 Happening without warning (6)
4 Recorded (moving images) on camera (6)

Gentle

92

ACROSS

1 Most secure; least dangerous (6)

4 Jogging or sprinting; managing (a company or team) (7)

5 Taken away; dislodged (7)

7 Gems; rocks (6)

DOWN

1 Learner who is taught by a teacher or tutor (7)

2 Activities that are enjoyable or amusing (3)

3 Members of a choir; an anagram of "resigns" (7)

6 Possess; an anagram of "won" (3)

Gentle

93

ACROSS

1 Come down to earth; end of many country names (4)

3 ___-hit wonder (3)

4 Forts; rooks on a chessboard (7)

5 Shed tears; weep (3)

6 (They) used to be (4)

DOWN

1 Romaine or iceberg; vegetable (7)

2 Six times fifteen (6)

3 Popular fruit (6)

Gentle

94

ACROSS

1 Tailless amphibian (4)
4 Lay down the ___ (3)
5 Person skilled in caring for the sick (5)
6 Cut of meat (5)
7 "To each ___ own" (3)
8 Blade's cutting side (4)

DOWN

1 This evening; later today (7)
2 To the opposite side (6)
3 Sparkle, especially like a star (7)
4 Traditional story or myth (6)

Gentle

95

ACROSS

1 Mothers and fathers (7)
4 Tanned animal skin, used for shoes, jackets, handbags, gloves, or sofas (7)
7 Female siblings (7)
9 Declines to accept (7)

DOWN

1 The opposite of "pushes" (5)
2 Uses a book (5)
3 Fasten with a decorative knot (3)
5 Parts of shoes (5)
6 Garden flowers (5)
8 Type of bag or cube (3)

Gentle

96

ACROSS

4 Large, edible crustacean (7)

5 One of the official languages of South Africa (7)

6 Gift; an anagram of "serpent" (7)

DOWN

1 Rural spot; nation (7)

2 Having no function or purpose (7)

3 Motives; explanations; causes (7)

Gentle

97

ACROSS

1 Known the world over (6)
4 Place for exhibiting art (7)
6 Brass wind instrument (7)
9 English capital; three-time Olympics host (6)

DOWN

1 Thick mist (3)
2 Fries are cooked in this (3)
3 Start a tennis match (5)
5 Fourth month of the year (5)
7 Adult boys (3)
8 Two times five (3)

Gentle

98

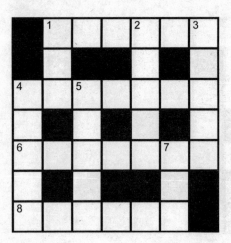

ACROSS

1 Teaching period (6)
4 Quite possibly; maybe (7)
6 "Gulliver's ___"; voyages (7)
8 Most modern; newest (6)

DOWN

1 Tell tall tales (3)
2 Milk-and-ice-cream drink (5)
3 Birds' homes (5)
4 Flower part (5)
5 Cook with dry heat (5)
7 Touched a match to; ignited (3)

Gentle

99

ACROSS

1 Feels at home (7)
4 Goal; direction (3)
6 Bottom of the sea (3)
7 Perform (3)
8 Atmosphere and outer space as viewed from Earth (3)
9 Twenty minus four (7)

DOWN

1 Soapy spheres (7)
2 Cargoes; a lot (5)
3 Bus or railway terminal (7)
5 Perhaps; possibly (5)

Gentle

100

ACROSS

1 Narrow-leaved green plants, often grown as lawns or cut as hay (5)
5 Upper surface of a room (7)
6 Made; generated (7)
7 Cooked in oil (5)

DOWN

2 Free something; let go (7)
3 Dusk; twilight (6)
4 Closer; an anagram of "earner" (6)

101

ACROSS

1 Less risky; comparatively trouble-free (5)
5 Came out into view (7)
6 Drive backward (7)
7 Tries; exams (5)

DOWN

1 Ledges for books (7)
2 Digits; arithmetical calculations (7)
3 Long, narrow crests; an anagram of "dirges" (6)
4 Something hidden; private (6)

Gentle

102

ACROSS

1 Public vehicle (3)
4 Move slowly and quietly (5)
6 Great noise (3)
7 Not feeling well; queasy (3)
8 Dirt or soil (5)
9 Foot digit (3)

DOWN

1 Crossing structure (6)
2 Painted structures of a stage set that are intended to suggest a particular place (7)
3 Great pleasure (7)
5 Officers of the law (6)

Gentle

103

ACROSS
1 Sweet, crisp fruit (5)
4 Young fox (3)
5 Explains; proves (5)
6 Time in grammar (5)
7 Popular form of transport (3)
8 Item of bed linen;
   type of knot (5)

DOWN
1 Lack (of something) (7)
2 Stick out; assignment (7)
3 Less difficult (6)
4 Prickly desert plant (6)

Gentle

104

ACROSS

3 In or to another country (6)
5 Not as thick (7)
8 February, April, and November, for example (6)

DOWN

1 Floating structure, especially if crudely made (4)
2 First part of the day (7)
4 Female rabbit (3)
6 Type of cured pork (3)
7 Move upward; the opposite of "sink" (4)

Gentle

ACROSS

4 Quaint country house (7)
5 "You ___ very clever!"; form of "to be" (3)
6 Consumed food (3)
7 Most wealthy (7)

DOWN

1 Pull to draw tight (7)
2 Homes for kings and queens (7)
3 Gobi, Sahara, or Antarctic, for example (6)
4 Leads (a meeting); seats (6)

Gentle

106

ACROSS

1 Scout's awards (6)
4 Imagined (7)
6 Short oars, used to propel or steer a canoe (7)
8 Spring or summer, for example (6)

DOWN

1 New flower (3)
2 Mother of your mother or father (7)
3 Part of a play; section of an act (5)
5 Lion's loud calls (5)
7 Earth's star (3)

Gentle

107

ACROSS

3 Express clearly in words; ___ment (5)
4 Move downward (7)
5 Welcome visitor; hotel customer (5)

DOWN

1 Emerged from an egg (7)
2 Popular snack, often roasted and salted (6)
3 Santa's mode of transport (6)

Gentle

108

ACROSS

1 Back of a book; bones in your back (5)

5 Source of stored energy (7)

6 Began (7)

7 They help Santa to make toys (5)

DOWN

2 Flora and fauna, ___ and animals (6)

3 Normal; instinctive (7)

4 Mediterranean country; site of the first Olympics (6)

Gentle

109

ACROSS

1 Gentler; not as harsh (6)
4 Land mass surrounded by water (6)
7 Selected; picked out (6)
9 Without sound; completely quiet (6)

DOWN

1 __ jump, or ___ slope (3)
2 Playfully make fun of (5)
3 Bad-mannered; not very nice (4)
5 Destroy or ruin (5)
6 ___ out; misbehaves (4)
8 Pecan, for example (3)

Gentle

110

ACROSS

4 Picture-taker (6)
6 Not in the home (7)
7 Pay heed to advice; hear (6)

DOWN

1 Most speedy (7)
2 Bring (letters, parcels, etc.) (7)
3 Bread and cake maker (5)
5 Earth, its countries and peoples (5)

Gentle

111

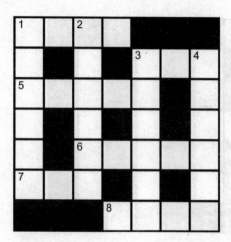

ACROSS

1 Clean with water and/or soap (4)
3 Upper limb of the human body (3)
5 One more time (5)
6 Not tightly fixed (5)
7 Owns; contains (3)
8 End parts of the leg (4)

DOWN

1 State of being rich (6)
2 Slow-moving creatures with shells (6)
3 An unspecified person (6)
4 Very short period of time; split second (6)

Gentle

112

ACROSS

1 Chills, as a beverage (4)
4 Light touch or stroke; bath or sink fitting (3)
6 Tooth doctor (7)
7 Grow old (3)
8 One of four in a square (4)

DOWN

2 Place where movies screen (6)
3 Sculpted human likenesses; carved figures, especially large ones (7)
5 Sent (a letter); an anagram of "despot" (6)

Gentle

113

ACROSS

1 Large numbers of people (6)
5 Hoping; type of well (7)
6 Line around the middle of the earth (7)
7 Steps for climbing up or down; an anagram of "larded" (6)

DOWN

2 Saved from danger (7)
3 Blow through pursed lips (7)
4 Substance used to sweeten cakes, cookies, etc. (5)
5 Cars have one of these on each corner (5)

Gentle

114

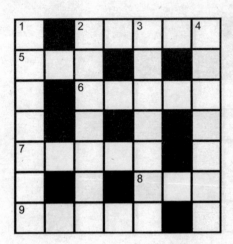

ACROSS

2 Incredibly great (5)

5 "___ this: that!" (3)

6 Very quick (5)

7 Garden barrier (5)

8 Definite article; one of ___ most common English words (3)

9 Female formal wear (5)

DOWN

1 Smelled quickly; "the dog ___ her dinner before she ate it" (7)

2 Out of the ordinary; unfamiliar (7)

3 Dolls on strings; marionettes (7)

4 Made smaller (7)

Gentle

115

ACROSS

1 Name of a book (5)
5 Goods vehicle (3)
6 Construction site lifter (5)
7 Once, ___, thrice (5)
8 In addition; as well (3)
9 Correct; the opposite of "left" (5)

DOWN

1 Entry passes; travel coupons (7)
2 Vehicle often seen in fields at harvest time (7)
3 Time of day between afternoon and night (7)
4 Look closely at; do a spot check (7)

Gentle

116

ACROSS

1 Curved chest bone (3)
4 Go; depart (5)
6 Long yellow fruits (7)
7 Recurring idea; many parties have one (5)
8 No longer wet (3)

DOWN

1 Burrowing mammal; long-eared pet (6)
2 Large piece of material used to wrap up a person for warmth (7)
3 Spooky house, said to be lived in by ghosts (7)
5 With very little effort (6)

Gentle

117

ACROSS

1 Not deep (7)
4 Painter or musician (6)
7 Change to ice (6)
8 Cared for (as a doctor would) (7)

DOWN

1 Distant sun (4)
2 One who plays a part (5)
3 The opposite of "in" (3)
5 Aroma, perfume (5)
6 Small ball on a necklace (4)
7 A long way (3)

Gentle

118

ACROSS

4 As, since (7)
5 Place where someone lives (7)
7 Skipper; head of a team (7)

DOWN

1 Give temporarily (4)
2 Tropical birds, often with the ability to mimic sounds (7)
3 Figures out (4)
5 Overhead curve (4)
6 Spoke; uttered (4)

Gentle

ACROSS

1 Idea (7)
4 Intended (5)
7 Measure of how far down something is (5)
9 Waxy lights (7)

DOWN

1 Vehicles on roads may cause a ___ jam (7)
2 Consume (3)
3 Makes contact with fingers (7)
5 Very angry or insane (3)
6 Quick swim (3)
8 Last section or part (3)

Gentle

120

ACROSS

1 Items on which food is served; an anagram of "staple" (6)
4 Ten, twenty, ___, forty (6)
7 Turn down, decline; rubbish (6)
8 Less strong (6)

DOWN

1 Cats, dogs, etc. (4)
2 Similar in appearance (5)
3 Put into words (3)
5 Wagon (5)
6 Grizzly or brown, for example (4)
7 Uncooked (3)

121

ACROSS

1 Bath___ (3)
5 Court command (5)
7 Feeling of rage (5)
8 Seize and hold firmly; wrap your mind around (5)
10 Carnival display (5)
11 Cooked slices of bread (5)
13 Projection from a cliff (5)
14 "What ___ I tell you?" (3)

DOWN

1 Grateful; appreciative (8)
2 Something to put groceries in (3)
3 No longer remembered (9)
4 Brainstorm results (5)
6 Duplicated; an anagram of "departee" (8)
9 ___ onto; grasps (5)
12 Also (3)

Challenging

122

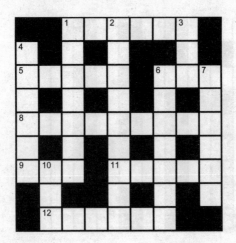

ACROSS

1 Wandered (6)
5 Goes in front (5)
6 Hamster, for example (3)
8 Cascade falling from a height (9)
9 Long, thin bar (3)
11 Language of Ancient Rome (5)
12 Fix, mend (6)

DOWN

1 Showed a response (7)
2 Island country (9)
3 Cease to live (3)
4 Less quick (6)
6 Wall surfacing (7)
7 Natural skill or aptitude (6)
10 Belonging to you and me (3)

Challenging

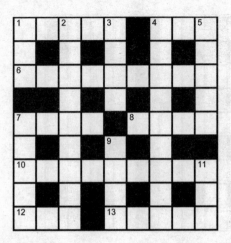

ACROSS

1 Cook's clothes protector (5)
4 Log of chocolate (3)
6 Flash in the sky (9)
7 Fifty percent (4)
8 Moved smoothly (4)
10 Section of writing (9)
12 Nervous; timid (3)
13 Calendar events (5)

DOWN

1 The opposite of "none" (3)
2 At even intervals of time (9)
3 Short, written message (4)
4 Dazzling, glittering (9)
5 Unyielding; stiff and unmoving (5)
7 Wishes; dreams (5)
9 Matured, like cheese (4)
11 Belonging to that man (3)

Challenging

124

ACROSS

1 Part of the arm (4)
4 Frozen rain (4)
6 Flower's "stick" (4)
7 Marsh plant (4)
8 Australian animal (5,4)
10 Quiet, serene (4)
11 Acquire through effort (4)
12 Daze; greatly surprise (4)
13 Lion's hair (4)

DOWN

2 Spaceman (9)
3 Barrier built by a beaver (3)
4 Clean by hard rubbing (5)
5 Hospital surgery (9)
9 Yellow fruit (5)
11 Place where heavy lifting is done (abbreviation) (3)

125

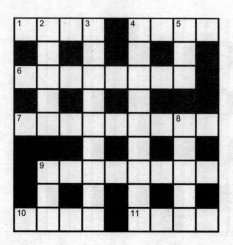

ACROSS

1 Part of a process; pace (4)
4 Sticky strip (4)
6 Gaining knowledge (8)
7 Measurement of depth in a three-dimensional object (9)
9 Increasing twofold (8)
10 Use a keyboard (4)
11 Small hard fruit (4)

DOWN

2 Biting tools (5)
3 Device that fills with air to slow your fall (9)
4 Three-sided shapes (9)
5 Clothesline pin; tent holder (3)
8 Touch, taste, or hearing, for example (5)
9 Dawn to dusk (3)

Challenging

126

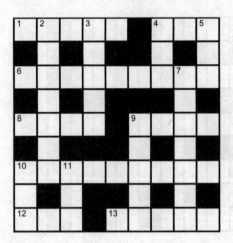

ACROSS

1 Metal carpentry pins (5)
4 Animal's foot (3)
6 Allowed (9)
8 Planet close to Earth (4)
9 Front part of the head (4)
10 Marine creature that can sting (9)
12 Massive; huge (3)
13 Garden buildings (5)

DOWN

2 Standard; normal (7)
3 Arms and legs (5)
4 Container for a plant (3)
5 Married (3)
7 Pardoned; let off (7)
9 Next after fourth (5)
10 Task; employment (3)
11 One of the supports for a table (3)

127

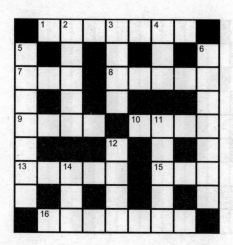

ACROSS

1 Puffing out air (7)
7 Count up (3)
8 Absolute; complete (5)
9 Water or swamp grass (4)
10 Ridge of water on the sea (4)
13 Item of furniture (5)
15 Young goat (3)
16 Went inside (7)

DOWN

2 Beaver's home (5)
3 In the company of (4)
4 Shelled tree-fruit (3)
5 Orange root vegetables (7)
6 So soon? (7)
11 This connects a foot to a leg (5)
12 Roll call reply (4)
14 Hot dog roll (3)

Challenging

128

ACROSS

2 Frog larva (7)
5 Dolphin's habitat (3)
6 Place in the ground (5)
7 Agitate; mix up (4)
10 Frozen water (3)
11 Challenge (4)
14 Baby sheep (5)
15 Harden (3)
16 Rotating windstorm (7)

DOWN

1 Makes a query (4)
2 Public passenger vehicle (4)
3 Tugged at; dragged (6)
4 Not as short (6)
8 Red salad ingredient (6)
9 Narrow strip of material (6)
12 As well; too (4)
13 Has breakfast or dinner (4)

129

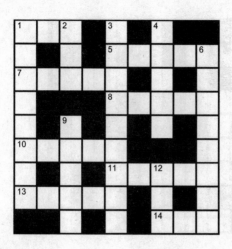

ACROSS

1 Wide inlet of the sea (3)
5 Gets together (5)
7 Shortest digit of the hand (5)
8 Brother of your father (5)
10 Drama set to music (5)
11 Steadiness; courage (5)
13 Witchcraft (5)
14 Deity (3)

DOWN

1 Washing area in the home (8)
2 "How are ___?" (3)
3 Hospital transport (9)
4 Get or bring (5)
6 Farm worker who looks after lambs and ewes (8)
9 Rule as king or queen (5)
12 Scrap of cloth (3)

Challenging

130

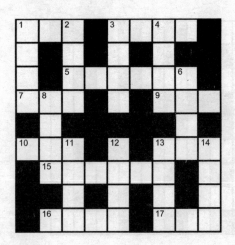

ACROSS

1 Quarrel (3)
3 Place to wash hands (4)
5 Bread units (6)
7 Fairylike creature (3)
9 Press a surface briefly with a cloth, without rubbing (3)
10 Page in an atlas (3)
13 Cerise, vermilion, or maroon (3)
15 Public procession (6)
16 Fewer in number (4)
17 Portion of land; auction item (3)

DOWN

1 Ready to eat (4)
2 Wild dog relative (4)
3 Stool or chair, e.g. (4)
4 Definitely require (4)
6 Free from danger (4)
8 Jump across; an anagram of "pale" (4)
11 Lacking brightness (4)
12 Baseball or table tennis items (4)
13 Not made up (4)
14 Earth; grime (4)

Challenging

131

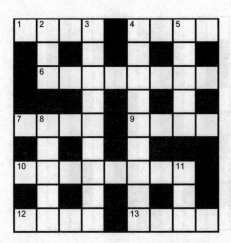

ACROSS

1 The Stars and Stripes or the Union Jack, for example (4)
4 Large bag for coal (4)
6 Root vegetables that can be boiled, fried, or baked (8)
7 Avoiding work; lazy (4)
9 Absolutely certain (4)
10 Groups related by blood or marriage (8)
12 Loud, explosive noise (4)
13 Slightly moist (4)

DOWN

2 Once around the track; drink with the tongue (3)
3 Group of people together in one place (9)
4 Sated; comfortable; had enough (9)
5 Jump over; easy to see (5)
8 Serious stage play; fuss (5)
11 Quantity (of money); add together (3)

Challenging

132

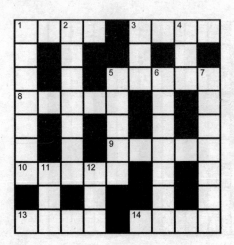

ACROSS

1 Successfully complete an exam or test (4)
3 Animal's feet (4)
5 Rise to one's feet (5)
8 Dairy product (5)
9 Marine mammals; tapes up tightly (5)
10 Compass point (5)
13 Intend; design (4)
14 Information about recent and important events (4)

DOWN

1 Snack food for the movies (7)
2 More sugary (7)
3 Cherry or peach stone (3)
4 Finish in first place (3)
5 Break suddenly into pieces (5)
6 Put in order (7)
7 Flowers commonly seen on a lawn (7)
11 Mainly nocturnal bird (3)
12 Unit of weight; great amount (3)

Challenging

133

ACROSS

5 Not with anyone else (5)
6 Have possession of (3)
7 Alternative (9)
10 People aged between thirteen and nineteen (9)
14 Device used to propel a boat (3)
15 Pedal; an anagram of "revel" (5)

DOWN

1 Solid; difficult (4)
2 Sport played with clubs (4)
3 Animal, ___, or mineral (9)
4 Nautical speed unit (4)
6 What borrowers do (3)
8 Very cold water (3)
9 And not (3)
10 Hammer, for example (4)
11 Body part with a drum (3)
12 Feeling of desire (4)
13 Kind; arrange (4)

Challenging

134

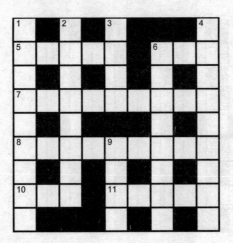

ACROSS

5 Rub; wipe out (5)
6 Fabric tint (3)
7 Put into another language (9)
8 Spots of water falling
   from the sky (9)
10 Expert (3)
11 Seat for one person (5)

DOWN

1 Previous day (9)
2 Periodic publication with
   pictures, stories, and articles (8)
3 Uses a needle (4)
4 Absolutely essential (9)
6 Slanting line, corner to corner (8)
9 Wharf or pier (4)

Challenging

135

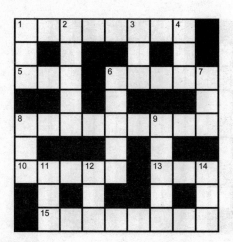

ACROSS

1 Perhaps or maybe (8)
5 As well; also (3)
6 What dinosaurs no longer do (5)
8 Become invisible (9)
10 Dizzy; frivolous (5)
13 Figured out; obtained (3)
15 Pouched mammal of Australia (8)

DOWN

1 Cooking vessel (3)
2 Halts; an anagram of "posts" (5)
3 Cardboard container; fight (3)
4 The opposite of "no" (3)
6 The opposite of "full" (5)
7 Dark, sticky liquid used
   to seal roads (3)
8 Turn up earth or soil (3)
9 Full of enthusiasm (5)
11 Pen fluid, used for writing (3)
12 Bear's winter haven (3)
14 Eight divided by four (3)

Challenging

136

ACROSS

- **4** Fertile spot in the desert (5)
- **6** Facial features (4)
- **7** Spinning toy; beat (3)
- **9** Handed over; supplied (9)
- **10** Watched (3)
- **12** Very small (4)
- **13** Move from a lower to a higher position (5)

DOWN

- **1** Preserved prehistoric remains, such as an ammonite (6)
- **2** Morsel; cut with the teeth (3)
- **3** Sour-tasting liquid used to pickle vegetables (7)
- **5** Unspecified person (7)
- **8** Defeated (6)
- **11** Path or route (3)

Challenging

137

ACROSS

2 Sticky tree sap (3)
6 The opposite of "him" (3)
7 Higher up (5)
8 Awesome; astounding (9)
11 Ninth month of the year (9)
16 Door securers; person's hair (5)
17 Aerial mammal; animal that inspired Bruce Wayne's costume (3)
18 Have a go (3)

DOWN

1 Use your teeth (4)
2 Big, wide smile (4)
3 Created; produced (4)
4 Cover for a house (4)
5 Device that rings when struck (4)
9 Single number (3)
10 Put into service (3)
11 Table condiment (4)
12 Choose from a group (4)
13 Compass point (4)
14 Child; small (4)
15 Cousins of mice (4)

Challenging

138

ACROSS

- **4** Half of six (5)
- **5** Hive-dwelling insect (3)
- **6** Fresh ___ (3)
- **7** Have a life; walk the Earth (5)
- **8** Small, social, hardworking insect (3)
- **9** Ocean (3)
- **10** Iron-based alloy; stainless ___ (5)
- **11** Use oars to move a boat (3)
- **12** Line of sunshine (3)
- **13** Parts of lists; things (5)

DOWN

- **1** Common or garden (8)
- **2** High temperature (4)
- **3** Cold-blooded, egg-laying vertebrates (8)
- **4** Buried gold, etc., marked with an "X" on a map (8)
- **5** Arm ornament (8)
- **10** Travel through water (4)

Challenging

139

ACROSS

1 Frozen projectile used in a friendly winter fight (8)
5 Second month in the year (8)
7 Very small spots (4)
10 Hurt; damage (4)
13 Highest in quality (8)
16 Opening for access; doorway (8)

DOWN

1 Observe; watch (3)
2 Rowing pole (3)
3 Shore of the sea (5)
4 Tier; an anagram of "early" (5)
5 Gave a meal to (3)
6 Small item inserted into a drill (3)
8 Liver, kidney, or heart (5)
9 Guide a vessel (5)
11 ___-inspiring (3)
12 Item of floor-covering (3)
14 Light brown shade (3)
15 That girl; her (3)

Challenging

140

ACROSS

1 The opposite of "right" (4)
3 Six-sided solid (4)
5 Public garden; leave a vehicle (4)
8 Small insects (4)
9 Frozen and slippery (3)
10 Clenched hand (4)
11 Take orders from (4)
12 Silvery metal (3)
13 Hillside hollow; cavern (4)
14 Transmitted; shipped (4)
17 Employs; takes advantage of (4)
18 Extremely (4)

DOWN

1 Pool length; Santa's visitor's seat (3)
2 Aimed at; in support of (3)
3 Drawing sticks (7)
4 In the space separating (7)
6 Occupants of a zoo (7)
7 Baby cats (7)
15 Organ of sight (3)
16 Plaything, such as a yo-yo or doll (3)

Challenging

141

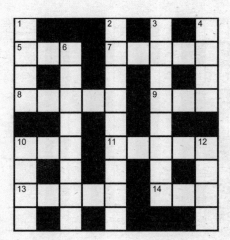

ACROSS

5 Eight plus two (3)
7 Chain of mountains; singer's vocal limits (5)
8 Twelfth of a year (5)
9 Outer part of a wheel (3)
10 Track event: shot ___; place in position (3)
11 Not long enough (5)
13 Unblocked; not clouded (5)
14 Male child (3)

DOWN

1 Thing; object (4)
2 Group of musicians (9)
3 The opposite of "tiny" (8)
4 Group working together; sports unit (4)
6 One less than twenty (8)
10 Single step; rate of speed (4)
12 Melody or harmony in a song (4)

Challenging

142

ACROSS

1 Finished; not under (4)
4 Nip, nibble; a mouthful (4)
6 Ascending (a hill or ladder) (8)
7 Appear to be (4)
8 Narrow way; country road (4)
10 Scout motto: "Be ___";
 made ready (8)
11 Odds and ___; remnants (4)
12 Specific piece of work;
 to-do list item (4)

DOWN

2 Worth; importance (5)
3 Brings to mind; thinks
 back on (9)
4 Very bright or vivid (9)
5 Pull hard or quickly (3)
9 Wants; requires (5)
10 Boiling or frying vessel (3)

Challenging

143

ACROSS

1 Living things collectively; "that's ___" (4)
3 Stand in line; serve at table in a restaurant (4)
7 Caught unawares; taken aback (9)
8 Called on someone (7)
11 Process of teaching (9)
12 On display; spotted (4)
13 The opposite of "beautiful" (4)

DOWN

1 Only remaining; an anagram of "salt" (4)
2 Tables, chairs, etc. (9)
4 Responding to a question (9)
5 Put things in good order; neaten (4)
6 Appearance, entrance (7)
9 Egg layers; female chickens (4)
10 Single, solitary (4)

Challenging

144

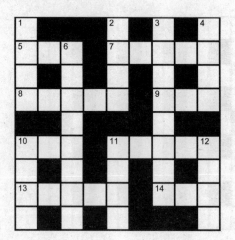

ACROSS

5 One of Santa's helpers (3)
7 Not conjoined (5)
8 Travel on ice (5)
9 Faintly visible (3)
10 Fireplace dust (3)
11 Large sailing vessels (5)
13 Blunder; trial and ___ (5)
14 Edge of a piece of cloth (3)

DOWN

1 Fountain, marker, and ballpoint (4)
2 Preserve; rescue (4)
3 Two slices of bread with something in between (8)
4 Stalk of a plant (4)
6 Plumage; covering for birds (8)
10 Length multiplied by width (4)
11 Coastal waves, breaking onto a beach (4)
12 Identical; ditto (4)

Challenging

145

ACROSS

1 Baseball player's headgear (3)
3 Chairs; an anagram of "asset" (5)
6 Go in (5)
7 Baby beaver or rabbit (3)
8 Needing to drink (7)
12 That male (3)
14 Of little size; lowercase (5)
15 Small lakes (5)
16 Cutting tool (3)

DOWN

1 People who work on a boat (4)
2 Eye covering worn by pirates (5)
3 Takes unawares; astonishes (9)
4 Noah's large boat (3)
5 Construction location (4)
9 Rips; an anagram of "stare" (5)
10 Use a tomahawk on;
   karate verb (4)
11 Took to the air (4)
13 Adult boy (3)

Challenging

146

ACROSS

3 Ski hill; an anagram of "poles" (5)
6 Acronym: light-emitting diode (3)
7 Impatient; keen (5)
8 Headwear item (3)
9 Correct; not false (4)
10 Index; an anagram of "silt" (4)
11 Unspecified (object or degree) (3)
13 Large place to shop (5)
14 Soldier or queen (3)
15 Pair of siblings born at
the same time (5)

DOWN

1 Of advanced years;
___ school (3)
2 In an orderly manner (6)
3 Private matters; an
anagram of "resects" (7)
4 Small vegetable,
grown in pods (3)
5 Periods of instruction (7)
8 Valentine symbols (6)
12 Unused; unfamiliar (3)
14 Too (3)

147

ACROSS

1 Home for bees (4)
4 Cover a gift; sandwich bread alternative (4)
7 Go headfirst into water (4)
9 Strong, thick cord (4)
10 Month following June (4)
11 Close one eye briefly (4)
12 Was sure about; "I ___ it!" (4)
14 Enter or escape through a hole or crack (4)
16 Simple toy on a string (2-2)
17 Exam; quiz (4)

DOWN

1 Possessed (3)
2 Female sheep (3)
3 Glass container for pickles (3)
5 Well-mannered; not rude (6)
6 Head support; violin part (4)
8 Low area between hills (6)
10 Funny story intended to make people laugh (4)
13 Came first (3)
14 Sale item; parking area (3)
15 Case containing a set of articles (3)

Challenging

148

ACROSS

1 Gently; quietly (6)
5 Like half of all numbers (4)
6 Corrosion on metal (4)
8 Adam's wife, in the Bible (3)
9 Immediately (3)
11 Frighten (5)
12 Bowler or fedora, for example (3)
14 Hen's produce (3)
15 Group of cows (4)
16 To the interior; having an enthusiasm for (4)
17 Stripy, wild cats (6)

DOWN

1 Formal spoken address, usually given to a crowd (6)
2 Large woodland area (6)
3 Still; however (3)
4 Nought; nothing (4)
7 Protection from the sun (5)
9 Sewing implement (6)
10 Covered carts that might be pulled by horses (6)
13 A parent's sister (4)
15 At high temperature (3)

ACROSS

3 Dressing for food (5)
5 Type of aircraft; hard, black rock (3)
6 Brave man (4)
7 Travel across snow (3)
8 Skeletal material; fibula or cranium (4)
9 Bird's home (4)
10 Removable cover (3)
11 On ___ (tense) (4)
12 Sleeping place (3)
13 Puzzle-solving aids (5)

DOWN

1 Touch quickly and gently with the flat of the hand (3)
2 At back of (6)
3 Extra helpings; divisions of a minute (7)
4 Puts on clothes (7)
7 Hand-pick; choose (6)
12 Ask for alms (3)

Challenging

150

ACROSS

1 Every; apiece (4)
4 In the past (4)
6 Sum up (3)
7 Not closed (4)
8 Having little or no light (4)
9 Replies (7)
11 Sight from a particular place (4)
13 A watch will tell you this (4)
14 Had a meal (3)
15 Becomes older (4)
16 Flower; dusty shade of pink (4)

DOWN

2 Seeming (9)
3 Units of length equal to four inches; used in measuring horses (5)
4 Not even (3)
5 Religious holiday in December (9)
10 Enrol; computer command (5)
12 Had existence (3)

151

ACROSS

1 Rainbow hue (4)
4 Farm animal; boar or sow (3)
6 Grain grown in a paddy (4)
7 Walk quietly; word after note (3)
8 Fake jewel material; an anagram of "tapes" (5)
10 Mumbai's country (5)
12 Order forbidding something (3)
13 Tidy (3)
14 Short, daytime sleep (3)
15 Piece of music, usually with words (4)

DOWN

2 Deposited an egg (4)
3 Big African creatures with trunks (9)
4 ___ and needles (4)
5 Very strong wind (4)
6 Water falling from the sky (4)
9 "You can say ___ again!" (4)
10 Press clothes; waffle ___ (4)
11 Slightly wet (4)
12 Building for farm animals (4)

Challenging

152

ACROSS

- 4 Fails to win (5)
- 6 Arrived (4)
- 7 Damp on grass (3)
- 9 Fairest; loveliest (9)
- 10 Like freshly applied paint; not dry (3)
- 12 Place to wash dishes (4)
- 13 Control a car; propel (5)

DOWN

- 1 More than enough (6)
- 2 Crimson or scarlet (3)
- 3 Lugged, borne (7)
- 5 Times of the year, each approximately three months long (7)
- 8 Overlooked; failed to hit (6)
- 11 Have a sample; give something a go (3)

Challenging

153

ACROSS

1 Limbs that aren't legs (4)
4 Squashed circle (4)
6 Pixie (3)
7 Proficient (4)
8 Amphibian that croaks (4)
9 Charts; orienteering items (4)
11 Long, audible breath (4)
13 Deep chasm or abyss (4)
15 Short piece (of video) (4)
17 Seek an answer to (3)
18 Item for Jack in a fairy tale (4)
19 Puts into words; Simon ___ (4)

DOWN

2 Steal from (3)
3 Edible parts of a sunflower (5)
4 Not switched on (3)
5 Included in; within (5)
7 Intend (3)
10 Make (someone) laugh (5)
11 Items worn with shoes (5)
12 Jump on one foot (3)
14 Device for creating a current of air (3)
16 Very chilly (3)

Challenging

154

ACROSS

1 Groups of students (7)
6 Not just "a"; part of "btw" (3)
7 Place in a certain arrangement (5)
8 Big-eyed nocturnal birds (4)
10 Not far (4)
12 Intelligent; sting (5)
14 Mouth part; edge (3)
15 Marine algae; sushi wrapper (7)

DOWN

1 Large, toothy reptile (9)
2 Assist (3)
3 Painfully sensitive (4)
4 Fixed look, sometimes glassy-eyed (5)
5 Disunited; split; pulled apart (9)
9 Coils; an anagram of "spool" (5)
11 The largest continent (4)
13 Lowland gorilla, for example (3)

Challenging

155

ACROSS

1 Turns quickly (5)
6 Erect a tent; area for games (5)
7 The opposite of "sad" (5)
9 Upper part of the body (4)
11 Do better than another
   in competition (4)
13 Small sticks, used by squirrels
   and birds to make nests (5)
14 Camera picture (abbreviation) (5)
15 Prodded with a finger or stick (5)

DOWN

2 State of calm; absence of war (5)
3 James Bond, for example (3)
4 Raised platform;
   developmental step (5)
5 Plot the course of (5)
8 Mini spacecraft; place
   for peas (3)
9 Lends a hand; makes it easier (5)
10 Missile shot by an archer (5)
11 Decorative tie (3)
12 Debate (5)
13 Upper part (3)

Challenging

156

ACROSS

1 Official travel document (8)
5 Had some food (3)
6 A smaller number of (5)
8 Searching or investigating an area (9)
10 Strolled in shallow water (5)
13 Form a knot or bow in a strip of material (3)
14 One of four playing-card suits (8)

DOWN

1 Location; vicinity (5)
2 Arranged in ascending levels (7)
3 Half of two (3)
4 One of the digits of the foot (3)
6 Become filled to overflowing (5)
7 Expressed on paper; jotted down (7)
9 Estimate on the basis of little or no information; suppose (5)
11 Compute a sum (3)
12 Historical period; chapter in history (3)

Challenging

157

ACROSS

1 Not that; "What's ___?" (4)
4 The opposite of "west" (4)
6 Santa's sleigh puller (8)
8 Answer to "Shall we?" (4)
10 State of disorder (4)
12 Eleven-a-side sport, also known as "soccer" (8)
14 Sea-going vessel (4)
15 Takes a seat (4)

DOWN

2 Animal that can be ridden; an anagram of "shore" (5)
3 Travels by yacht (5)
4 Conclusion; bring to a halt (3)
5 Rotates; twists (5)
7 Cyclops's single feature (3)
8 Raises up (5)
9 One plus one (3)
10 Breakfast, lunch, and dinner (5)
11 Divide into two equal portions (5)
13 Pointed end of something; an anagram of "pit" (3)

Challenging

158

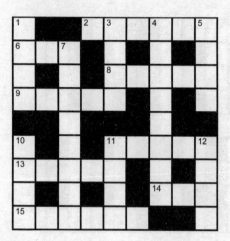

ACROSS

2 Very top of a mountain (6)
6 Young tiger (3)
8 Part of the movie crowd (5)
9 Rate of travel (5)
11 Metal currency (5)
13 Expertise; ability (5)
14 Give permission; allow (3)
15 Wrote one's name on; an anagram of "design" (6)

DOWN

1 Parts of a play; behaves (4)
3 Secondhand; no longer new (4)
4 Cloth used to make clothes (8)
5 Water from the eye; rip (4)
7 Shattering; wrecking (8)
10 Puts questions to (4)
11 Hint (4)
12 Uses a chair (4)

Challenging

159

ACROSS

1 Percussion instrument (4)
6 Machine, can be steam or combustion (6)
7 Search for prey (4)
8 Dropped to the floor (4)
10 Better than average (4)
12 Sums up (4)
13 Heavenly beings (6)
14 Certain; an anagram of "ruse" (4)

DOWN

2 Chosen path (5)
3 Iron or copper, for example (5)
4 Keyboard instrument (5)
5 Listened to (5)
8 Last game of a competition (5)
9 Breathing organs (5)
10 Stained ___ (5)
11 More senior in years (5)

Challenging

160

ACROSS

1 Coastal crustacean; sideways scuttler (4)
4 Indication; put your name to (4)
6 Medicinal lotion (8)
7 Not new; an anagram of "dues" (4)
9 Santa's toy holder (4)
11 Garments, apparel (8)
13 Finishes; completes (4)
14 Facial disguise; catcher's protection (4)

DOWN

2 Straps used to control a horse (5)
3 Except for (3)
4 Paces; an anagram of "pests" (5)
5 Understood, as a joke; obtained (3)
8 Ways in and out (5)
10 Ice cream holders (5)
11 Be permitted to; is able to (3)
12 Sing with closed lips (3)

Challenging

161

ACROSS

2 Ebb and flow of the ocean (4)
5 Feel concern for another (4)
6 Underground part of a plant (4)
7 After the arranged time; "It's never too ___ to say sorry" (4)
8 Extraordinarily good (9)
11 Covers (a cake) with frosting (4)
12 On the positive side of a scale; arithmetical sign (4)
13 Make with wool (4)
14 Part of the mouth; an anagram of "smug" (4)

DOWN

1 Feline creature (3)
2 Blabs; spills the beans (5)
3 Healthy physical or mental activity (8)
4 Moving aimlessly (8)
5 Grain used to make tortillas (4)
9 Long, pointed teeth sticking out from the mouth of an elephant (5)
10 Be at an angle; lean or slope (4)
12 Object used in the game of bowling (3)

Solutions

1

B	L	U	E	
	U	X		
K	N	O	T	S
	C		R	
	H	E	A	D

2

E		R		S
Q	U	I	L	T
U		N		A
A	N	G	R	Y
L		S		S

3

		B	U	D
S		U		O
T	H	I	N	G
E		L		S
M	U	D		

4

P	I	L	O	T
	G		F	
	L	E	T	
	O		E	
F	O	U	N	D

5

	P	I	C	K
	L		H	
C	A	B	I	N
	T		L	
W	E	E	D	

6

	S	T	I	R
		H		A
J	U	I	C	Y
A		N		
M	A	K	E	

7

B	R	A	V	E
L		L		N
O	L	I	V	E
O		E		M
M	I	N	T	Y

8

		C		B
F	R	O	Z	E
I		U		N
N	I	G	H	T
D		H		

9

S	Q	U	I	D
	U		D	
G	A	M	E	S
	C		A	
S	K	I	L	L

10

	B		C	
M	E	D	A	L
	G	U	M	
P	A	G	E	S
	N		L	

11

B			S	
L	I	G	H	T
A		E		I
C	O	M	I	C
K			K	

12

O		W		
B	L	I	N	K
E		T		I
Y	A	C	H	T
		H		E

Solutions

13

A	B	L	E	
	R		I	
J	U	D	G	E
	S		H	
	H	A	T	S

14

P		S		H
L	U	C	K	Y
U		A		E
M	E	L	O	N
E		E		A

15

		G	U	M
E		U		A
C	H	I	L	D
H		L		E
O	U	T		

16

S	L	O	P	E
	U		U	
	C	O	T	
	K		O	
H	Y	M	N	S

17

	B	A	T	H
	A		H	
S	N	A	I	L
	J		C	
Y	O	L	K	

18

	P	U	R	R
		S		U
C	L	I	M	B
U		N		
B	U	G	S	

Solutions

19

P	O	W	E	R
I		A		O
L	I	L	A	C
E		T		K
D	I	Z	Z	Y

20

		B		P
G	R	A	Z	E
A		S		C
T	H	I	N	K
E		N		

21

H	U	M	A	N
	N		C	
I	T	C	H	Y
	I		E	
G	L	I	D	E

22

	G		H	
L	E	M	O	N
	T		I	
B	O	X	E	S
	N		Y	

23

C			P	
L	O	C	A	L
O		A		A
W	I	N	D	Y
N			S	

24

A		G		
C	H	I	N	A
I		V		R
D	R	E	A	M
		N		S

Solutions

25

S	T	O	P	
	H		I	
R	I	V	E	R
	N		C	
	G	O	E	S

26

S		W		G
P	I	A	N	O
A		T		O
D	U	C	K	S
E		H		E

27

		J	A	W
I		U		A
D	R	I	N	K
E		C		E
A	P	E		

28

F	L	I	E	S
	A		G	
	B	O	Y	
	E		P	
C	L	O	T	H

29

	C	U	R	L
	R		O	
V	A	L	U	E
	Z		N	
D	Y	E	D	

30

	B	I	R	D
		M		E
C	H	A	I	N
U		G		
P	E	E	L	

Solutions

31

S	C	R	U	B
I		O		E
Z	E	B	R	A
E		O		C
D	I	T	C	H

32

		B		O
T	R	A	I	N
A		N		L
M	U	D	D	Y
E		S		

33

C	L	I	F	F
	A		I	
F	U	N	N	Y
	G		D	
C	H	A	S	E

34

	T		J	
R	E	L	A	X
	D		I	P
I	D	E	A	S
	Y		N	

35

P				A
R	O	B	I	N
I		U		G
C	A	N	O	E
E				L

36

C		H		
A	D	U	L	T
M		R		O
P	A	R	T	Y
		Y		S

37

A	D	D	S	
	O		T	
M	I	N	E	R
	N		E	
	G	I	R	L

38

S		P		M
H	E	L	L	O
A		A		T
P	I	N	C	H
E		E		S

39

		R	A	M
T		O		I
U	S	U	A	L
B		G		K
A	S	H		

40

C	L	O	C	K
	O		A	
	W	E	B	
	E		I	
F	R	O	N	T

41

	S	I	N	G
	P		I	
L	A	R	G	E
	R		H	
M	E	L	T	

42

	S	W	A	N
		I		O
O	W	N	E	D
U		G		
R	U	S	H	

172

Solutions

43

B	U	N	C	H
E		A		U
L	I	M	I	T
O		E		C
W	I	D	T	H

44

		V		U
B	R	I	N	G
E		S		L
S	H	I	N	Y
T		T		

45

S	P	O	K	E
	E		I	
P	A	I	N	T
	R		D	
C	L	O	S	E

46

	O		B	
A	T	L	A	S
	H		I	D
H	E	D	G	E
	R		E	

47

P				S
U	P	S	E	T
P		E		O
P	L	A	I	N
Y				E

48

S	U		G	
S	W	I	N	G
E		A		R
D	A	N	C	E
		T		W

173

49

S		C		T
T	H	R	E	E
A		O		A
M	U	S	I	C
P		S		H

50

			B	A	D
S			U		E
K	I	N	G	S	
I			N		K
P	A	Y			

51

A	B	L	E	
	L		R	
C	U	R	R	Y
	N		O	
	T	E	R	M

52

S	A	D		O		
H		O	C	C	U	R
A		L		T		A
R	I	P		O	U	T
K		H		B		T
S	L	I	C	E		L
		N		R	Y	E

53

		Q	U	E	E	N
E	M	U		X		E
N		A	P	P	L	E
A		R		L		D
M	O	T	T	O		L
E		E		D	O	E
	L	A	R	G	E	

54

F			O			
I	C	I	C	L	E	
V			T		Y	
E	N	J	O	Y	E	D
	E		P			U
	T	H	U	M	B	S
			S			T

55

```
   E   P   H
C O M P A R E
L   P   N   A
I C E   C U T
M   R   A   E
B L O C K E D
S   R   E
```

56

```
R H Y M E S
A       O   P
T H U N D E R
  O   K   L
Q U I E T L Y
  S   Y     E
E A S E L S
```

57

```
      C
  G L O V E
  R   L   V
B O U L D E R
  W   E   R
  L U C K Y
      T
```

58

```
  S T A G E S
  E   R   T
F A C T O R Y
R   R   U   L
E X A M P L E
S   W     E
H A L V E D
```

59

```
C O M P A S S
L   A     N
O   G A P   E
S K I   O W E
E   C A R   Z
S       C   E
T O U C H E D
```

60

```
  E Q U A L
  E   U   M
A F R I C A N
  F   C   Z
C O O K I E S
  R   L   D
S T A Y S
```

Solutions

61

```
. W E A R S .
A R . U . T .
C H A P T E R
C . P . H . E
E X P L O D E
N . E . R . T
T I D E S . .
```

62

```
. . . A . . A
. W I L L O W
. H . A . . A
J O U R N E Y
O . . M . A .
I N S E C T .
N . . D . . .
```

63

```
P A T I E N T
U . . N . . E
M U C K Y . A
P . O . O . C
K . D O U G H
I . . W . . E
N U C L E A R
```

64

```
B U C K E T .
E . H . . A .
E D I T O R .
S . L . L . A
. F L Y I N G
. I . . V . E
. T H R E A D
```

65

```
S T I F F . A
T . N . L O G
R A D I O . A
O . O . W . I
K . O N I O N
E A R . N . S
D . S I G H T
```

66

```
T E A . D . .
A . C O O K S
U . R . U . L
G O O D B Y E
H . B . L . E
T R A C E . V
. . T . D U E
```

Solutions

67

S	I	M	I	L	A	R
H		A		N		
O	B	J	E	C	T	
E		O		A		I
	G	R	O	U	N	D
	E			S		L
A	T	H	L	E	T	E

68

M	O	T	H	S		
	P		E		S	
J	E	A	L	O	U	S
	N		P		M	
P	E	R	F	U	M	E
	D		U		E	
	A	L	A	R	M	

69

	C	H	E	W	E	D
	A		H		E	
	B	R	E	E	Z	E
S		O		R		P
P	I	C	K	E	D	
O		K			Y	
T	I	S	S	U	E	

70

	B		H		B	
	D	E	C	I	D	E
C		C		G		R
A	N	O	T	H	E	R
T		M		E		Y
C	H	E	E	S	E	
H		S		T		

71

C	A	R	D			
U		E		B	O	W
C	O	M	M	A		H
K		I		K		E
O		N	O	I	S	E
O	L	D		N		L
			E	G	G	S

72

P	A	I	D			
	M		O	A	K	
	O		U		A	
H	U	S	B	A	N	D
	N		L		S	
	T	E	E		A	
		D	A	S	H	

Solutions

73

	A	N	C	H	O	R
		O		A		I
A	L	T	E	R	E	D
I		H		V		E
S	P	I	D	E	R	S
L		N		S		
E	I	G	H	T	Y	

74

U		B	A	S	I	C
P	I	E		Q		U
R		D	R	U	M	S
I		T		E		H
G	U	I	D	E		I
H		M		Z	O	O
T	H	E	R	E		N

75

	W	H	A	L	E	S
	E		R			A
F	A	S	T	E	S	T
	R			W		
P	Y	R	A	M	I	D
O			I		F	
P	A	R	R	O	T	

76

V			C		H	
E	U	R	O	P	E	
R			N		R	
B	O	U	N	C	E	D
	V		E			R
	E	S	C	A	P	E
	N		T			W

77

S	H	O	W	E	R	
T		P		U		
E	L	E	G	A	N	T
A		N		L		R
M	A	S	S	I	V	E
	C			E		E
	T	E	N	N	I	S

78

W		U		N		
O	P	I	N	I	O	N
R		U		S		
D	R	E	S	S	E	D
	A		U			E
B	R	E	A	T	H	E
	E		L			R

Solutions

79

```
S   F   C
P O L L E N
A   O   R   G
C H A T T E R
E   T   A   E
  R E C I P E
    D   N   N
```

80

```
    W       M
  P I C N I C
    S     C O W
    H O T E L
P E N     D
    S C A R E D
    E       R
```

81

```
  V E S S E L
    X   W   A
    S P R E A D
T   L   A   Y
H E A L T H
E   I   E
M I N E R S
```

82

```
C O B W E B S
  D     A   A
  D R A G O N
A O   L   D
T R A V E L
O D   E
M E S S A G E
```

83

```
    C   M U G
S T O R Y   R
E   S   S   O
C A T   T O W
O   U   E   T
N   M A R C H
D U E   Y
```

84

```
S T E P   S
  R   R I C H
  A   E   I
K I T C H E N
  N   I   N
B E D S   C
  D   E V E N
```

179

Solutions

85

C			B	O	T	H
H	A	S		L		E
O		M	O	D	E	L
O		I		E		P
S	E	L	L	S		I
E		E		T	A	N
S	I	D	E			G

86

	M		P		
H	O	R	S	E	S
	N		P	A	C	K
	D		I		H
B	A	L	L		O
	Y	E	L	L	O	W
	T				L

87

C	R	O	P			
	E		R	E	S	T
	P		I		P	
R	A	I	N	B	O	W
	I		T		K	
F	R	E	E		E	
			R	U	N	G

88

		S	P	I	N
G	A	S		R		E
A		T	W	I	C	E
R		R		Z		D
A	L	I	V	E		L
G		P		S	E	E
E	V	E	R			

89

B	R	U	S	H	
U		N		O	A	R
T	W	I	S	T		U
T		F		T		N
O		O	C	E	A	N
N	O	R		S		E
		M	O	T	O	R

90

O	P	P	O	S	E	D
	I		M		A
A	N	C	I	E	N	T
T		O		L		E
T	U	R	T	L	E	S
I		A			G	
C	O	L	L	E	G	E

Solutions

91

Solutions

97

F	A	M	O	U	S	
O		I		E		
G	A	L	L	E	R	Y
	P			V		
T	R	U	M	P	E	T
	I		E		E	
	L	O	N	D	O	N

98

	L	E	S	S	O	N
	I			H		E
P	E	R	H	A	P	S
E		O		K		T
T	R	A	V	E	L	S
A		S				I
L	A	T	E	S	T	

99

B	E	L	O	N	G	S
U		O				T
B		A	I	M		A
B	E	D		A	C	T
L		S	K	Y		I
E				B		O
S	I	X	T	E	E	N

100

	G	R	A	S	S	
	N		E		U	
C	E	I	L	I	N	G
	A		E		S	
C	R	E	A	T	E	D
	E		S		T	
F	R	I	E	D		

101

	S	A	F	E	R	
S		H		I		
E	M	E	R	G	E	D
C		L		U		G
R	E	V	E	R	S	E
E		E		E		S
T	E	S	T	S		

102

B	U	S		D		
R		C	R	E	E	P
I		E		L		O
D	I	N		I	L	L
G		E		G		I
E	A	R	T	H		C
		Y		T	O	E

Solutions

103

	A	P	P	L	E
C	U	B		R		A
A		S	H	O	W	S
C		E		J		I
T	E	N	S	E		E
U		C		C	A	R
S	H	E	E	T		

104

R		M			
A	B	R	O	A	D
F		R		O	
T	H	I	N	N	E	R
	A		I		I
	M	O	N	T	H	S
		G			E

105

	S		P		D
C	O	T	T	A	G	E
H		R		L		S
A	R	E		A	T	E
I		T		C		R
R	I	C	H	E	S	T
S		H		S	

106

B	A	D	G	E	S
U		R		C	
D	R	E	A	M	E	D
	O		N		N
P	A	D	D	L	E	S
	R		M		U
	S	E	A	S	O	N

107

		H		P	
	S	T	A	T	E
	L		T		A
D	E	S	C	E	N	D
	I		H		U
	G	U	E	S	T
	H		D	

108

S	P	I	N	E	
	L		A		G
B	A	T	T	E	R	Y
	N		U		E
S	T	A	R	T	E	D
	S		A		C
	E	L	V	E	S

Solutions

109

	S	O	F	T	E	R
	K		E		U	
	I	S	L	A	N	D
A		P		S		E
C	H	O	S	E	N	
T		I		U		
S	I	L	E	N	T	

110

		F		D		B
	C	A	M	E	R	A
W		S		L		K
O	U	T	S	I	D	E
R		E		V		R
L	I	S	T	E	N	
D		T		R		

111

W	A	S	H			
E		N		A	R	M
A	G	A	I	N		O
L		I		Y		M
T		L	O	O	S	E
H	A	S		N		N
		F	E	E	T	

112

I	C	E	S			
	I		T	A	P	
	N		A		O	
D	E	N	T	I	S	T
	M		U		T	
A	G	E		E		
		S	I	D	E	

113

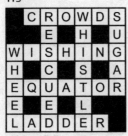

	C	R	O	W	D	S
		E		H		U
W	I	S	H	I	N	G
H		C		S		A
E	Q	U	A	T	O	R
E		E		L		
L	A	D	D	E	R	

114

S		S	U	P	E	R
N	O	T		U		E
I		R	A	P	I	D
F		A		P		U
F	E	N	C	E		C
E		G		T	H	E
D	R	E	S	S		D

115

T	I	T	L	E		I
I		R		V	A	N
C	R	A	N	E		S
K		C		N		P
E		T	W	I	C	E
T	O	O		N		C
S		R	I	G	H	T

116

R	I	B		H		
A		L	E	A	V	E
B		A		U		A
B	A	N	A	N	A	S
I		K		T		I
T	H	E	M	E		L
		T		D	R	Y

117

S	H	A	L	L	O	W
T		C			U	
A	R	T	I	S	T	
R		O		C		B
	F	R	E	E	Z	E
	A			N		A
T	R	E	A	T	E	D

118

	L		P		G
B	E	C	A	U	S	E
	N		R		T
A	D	D	R	E	S	S
R		O		A	
C	A	P	T	A	I	N
H		S		D	

119

T	H	O	U	G	H	T
R		S			O	
A	I	M	E	D		U
F		A		I		C
F		D	E	P	T	H
I			N		E	
C	A	N	D	L	E	S

120

P	L	A	T	E	S	
E		L			A	
T	H	I	R	T	Y	
S		K		R		B
	R	E	F	U	S	E
	A			C		A
W	E	A	K	E	R	

121

```
T U B . . F . I .
H . A . O R D E R
A N G E R . E . E
N . . . G R A S P
K . H . O . S . E
F L O A T . . . A
U . L . . T O A S T
L E D G E . N . E
. S . . N . D I D
```

122

```
. . R O A M E D .
S . E . U . . . I
L E A D S . P E T
O . C . T . L . A
W A T E R F A L L
E . E . A . S . E
R O D . L A T I N
U . . . I . E . T
. R E P A I R . .
```

123

```
A P R O N . B A R
L . E . O . R . I
L I G H T N I N G
. . U . E . L . I
H A L F . S L I D
O . A . A . I . I
P A R A G R A P H
E . L . E . N . I
S H Y . D A T E S
```

124

```
H A N D . S N O W
. S . A . C . P .
S T E M . R E E D
. R . . . U . R .
K O A L A B E A R
. N . E . . . T .
C A L M . G A I N
. U . O . Y . O .
S T U N . M A N E
```

125

```
S T E P . T A P E
. E . A . R . E .
L E A R N I N G
. T . A . A .
T H I C K N E S S
. . H . G . E .
D O U B L I N G
. A . T . E . S
T Y P E . S E E D
```

126

```
N A I L S . P A W
. V . I . . O . E
P E R M I T T E D
. R . B . . X .
M A R S . F A C E
. G . . . I . U .
J E L L Y F I S H
O . E . . T . E
B I G . S H E D S
```

Solutions

127

	B	L	O	W	I	N	G	
C	O		I		U		A	
A	D	D		T	O	T	A	L
R		G		H			R	
R	E	E	D		W	A	V	E
O		H		N		A		
T	A	B	L	E		K	I	D
S		U		R		L		Y
	E	N	T	E	R	E	D	

128

A		T	A	D	P	O	L	E
S	E	A			U		O	
K		X		P	L	A	N	T
S	T	I	R		L		G	
	O		I	C	E		E	
	M		B		D	A	R	E
L	A	M	B	S		L		A
	T		O			S	E	T
T	O	R	N	A	D	O		S

129

B	A	Y		A		F		
A		O		M	E	E	T	S
T	H	U	M	B		T		H
H				U	N	C	L	E
R		R		L		H		P
O	P	E	R	A				H
O		I		N	E	R	V	E
M	A	G	I	C		A		R
	N		E		G	O	D	

130

R	O	W		S	I	N	K	
I		O		E		E		
P		L	O	A	V	E	S	
E	L	F		T		D	A	B
	E					F		
M	A	P		B		R	E	D
	P	A	R	A	D	E		I
		L		T		A		R
L	E	S	S		L	O	T	

131

F	L	A	G		S	A	C	K
	A		A		A		L	
	P	O	T	A	T	O	E	S
		H		I		A		
I	D	L	E		S	U	R	E
	R		R		F			
F	A	M	I	L	I	E	S	
	M		N		E		U	
B	A	N	G		D	A	M	P

132

P	A	S	S		P	A	W	S
O		W			I		I	
P		E		S	T	A	N	D
C	R	E	A	M		R		A
O		T		A		R		I
R		E		S	E	A	L	S
N	O	R	T	H		N		I
	W		O			G		E
P	L	A	N		N	E	W	S

133

H	G	V			K	
A	L	O	N	E		O	W	N
R		G		W		O
D	I	F	F	E	R	E	N	T
	C		T		O
T	E	E	N	A	G	E	R	S
O		A		B		N	O
O	A	R		L	E	V	E	R
L			E		Y	T

134

Y		M		S				N
E	R	A	S	E		D	Y	E
S		G		W		I		C
T	R	A	N	S	L	A	T	E
E		Z			G		S
R	A	I	N	D	R	O	P	S
D		N		O		N		A
A	C	E		C	H	A	I	R
Y			K		L	L	Y

135

P	O	S	S	I	B	L	Y
O		T		O		E
T	O	O		E	X	I	S	T
		P		M			A
D	I	S	A	P	P	E	A	R
I			T		A
G	I	D	D	Y		G	O	T
	N		E		E		W
	K	A	N	G	A	R	O	O

136

		F		B
	V		O	A	S	I	S
L	I	P	S			T	O	P
	N		S		B		M
D	E	L	I	V	E	R	E	D
	G		L		A		O
S	A	W			T	I	N	Y
	R	A	I	S	E		E
	Y			N

137

C		G	U	M		R		B
H	E	R		A	B	O	V	E
E		I		D		O		L
W	O	N	D	E	R	F	U	L
	N				S
S	E	P	T	E	M	B	E	R
A		I		A		A		A
L	O	C	K	S		B	A	T
T		K		T	R	Y		S

138

		O		H				R
T	H	R	E	E			B	E	E
R		D		A	I	R		P
E	X	I	S	T		A	N	T
A		N				C		I
S	E	A		S	T	E	E	L
U		R	O	W		L		E
R	A	Y		I	T	E	M	S
E			M		T

Solutions

139

```
  S N O W B A L L
  E   A   E     A
F E B R U A R Y
E   I   C     E
D O T S   H A R M
  R   T   W     A
G R E A T E S T
A   E   A     H
E N T R A N C E
```

140

```
L E F T   C U B E
A   O     R   E
P A R K   A N T S
N   I C Y   W
F I S T   O B E Y
M   T I N   E
C A V E   S E N T
L   N     Y   O
U S E S   V E R Y
```

141

```
I       O   E   T
T E N   R A N G E
E   I   C   O   A
M O N T H   R I M
    E   E   M
P U T   S H O R T
A   E   T   U   U
C L E A R   S O N
E   N   A       E
```

142

```
O V E R   B I T E
  A   E   R   U
C L I M B I N G
  U   E   L
S E E M   L A N E
    B   I   E
  P R E P A R E D
  A   R   N   D
E N D S   T A S K
```

143

```
L I F E   W A I T
A   U   A   N   I
S U R P R I S E D
T   N   R   W   Y
  V I S I T E D
H   T   V   R   O
E D U C A T I O N
N   R   L   N   L
S E E N   U G L Y
```

144

```
P     S   S   S
E L F   A P A R T
N   E   V   N   E
S K A T E   D I M
    T       W
A S H   S H I P S
R   E   U   C   A
E R R O R   H E M
A   S   F       E
```

145

C	A	P		S	E	A	T	S
R		A		U		R		I
E	N	T	E	R		K	I	T
W		C		P				E
	T	H	I	R	S	T	Y	
C		I		E		F		
H	I	M		S	M	A	L	L
O		A		E		R		E
P	O	N	D	S		S	A	W

146

	O			N			
	S	L	O	P	E		L
L	E	D		E	A	G	E	R
	C		H	A	T		S
T	R	U	E		L	I	S	T
	E		A	N	Y		O
S	T	O	R	E		A	N	T
	S		T	W	I	N	S	
			S			D	

147

H	I	V	E		J		
A			W	R	A	P		N
D	I	V	E		R	O	P	E
		A			L		C
J	U	L	Y		W	I	N	K
O		L				T	
K	N	E	W		L	E	A	K
E		Y	O	Y	O			I
		N		T	E	S	T

148

S	O	F	T	L	Y		Z
P		O			E	V	E	N
E		R	U	S	T		R
E	V	E		H		N	O	W
C		S	C	A	R	E		A
H	A	T		D		E	G	G
	U		H	E	R	D		O
I	N	T	O			L		N
T		T	I	G	E	R	S

149

	P			B
S	A	U	C	E		D
J	E	T			H	E	R	O
	C		S	K	I		E
B	O	N	E		N	E	S	T
	N		L	I	D		S
E	D	G	E			B	E	D
	S		C	L	U	E	S
		T			G

150

E	A	C	H		O	N	C	E
P		A	D	D		H
O	P	E	N		D	A	R	K
E		D			I
A	N	S	W	E	R	S
R			N		T
V	I	E	W		T	I	M	E
N		A	T	E		A
A	G	E	S		R	O	S	E

Solutions

151

	B	L	U	E			P	I	G
	A		L			I		A	
	R	I	C	E		N		L	
P	A	D		P	A	S	T	E	
	I		H			H			
I	N	D	I	A		B	A	N	
R		A		N	E	A	T		
O		M		T		R			
N	A	P		S	O	N	G		

152

			P			R			
	C		L	O	S	E	S		
C	A	M	E			D	E	W	
	R		N		M		A		
P	R	E	T	T	I	E	S	T	
	I		Y		S		O		
W	E	T			S	I	N	K	
	D	R	I	V	E		S		
	Y				D				

153

A	R	M	S		O	V	A	L
	O		E	L	F		M	
A	B	L	E		F	R	O	G
I		D			N			
M	A	P	S		S	I	G	H
	M		O		O		O	
G	U	L	F		C	L	I	P
	S		A	S	K		C	
B	E	A	N		S	A	Y	S

154

C	L	A	S	S	E	S		S
R		I		O		T	H	E
O	R	D	E	R		A		P
C		E		E		R		A
O	W	L	S		N	E	A	R
D		O		A				A
I		O		S	M	A	R	T
L	I	P		I		P		E
E		S	E	A	W	E	E	D

155

S	P	I	N	S		S		C
	E			P	I	T	C	H
H	A	P	P	Y		A		A
	C		O		A	G		R
H	E	A	D		B	E	A	T
E		R		O		R		
L		R		T	W	I	G	S
P	H	O	T	O		U		
S		W		P	O	K	E	D

156

P	A	S	S	P	O	R	T	
L		T		N		O		
A	T	E		F	E	W	E	R
C		P		L		R		
E	X	P	L	O	R	I	N	G
	E		O		O			U
W	A	D	E	D		T	I	E
	D		R		E			S
	D	I	A	M	O	N	D	S

Solutions

157

T	H	I	S		E	A	S	T
	O		A		N		U	
	R	E	I	N	D	E	E	R
	S		L		Y		N	
L	E	T	S		M	E	S	S
I		W		E		P		
F	O	O	T	B	A	L	L	
T		I		L		I		
S	H	I	P		S	I	T	S

158

A			S	U	M	M	I	T
C	U	B		S		A		E
T		R		E	X	T	R	A
S	P	E	E	D		E		R
		A				R		
A		K		C	O	I	N	S
S	K	I	L	L		A		I
K		N		U		L	E	T
S	I	G	N	E	D			S

159

D	R	U	M			P		H
	O		E	N	G	I	N	E
H	U	N	T			A		A
	T		A			N		R
F	E	L	L		G	O	O	D
I		U		L		L		
N		N		A	D	D	S	
A	N	G	E	L	S		E	
L		S		S	U	R	E	

160

C	R	A	B		S	I	G	N
	E		U		T		O	
O	I	N	T	M	E	N	T	
	N			P				
U	S	E	D		S	A	C	K
		O				O		
	C	L	O	T	H	I	N	G
	A		R		U		E	
E	N	D	S		M	A	S	K

161

		C		T	I	D	E	
D		C	A	R	E			X
R	O	O	T		L	A	T	E
I		R		L			R	
F	A	N	T	A	S	T	I	C
T		U		I			I	
I	C	E	S		P	L	U	S
N		K	N	I	T			E
G	U	M	S		N